You Speak in Constellations
Poems by the Foyle Young
Poets of the Year 2020

THE**POETRY**SOCIETY

Acknowledgements

The Poetry Society is deeply grateful for the generous funding and commitment of the Foyle Foundation, and to Arts Council England for its ongoing support.

We would like to thank: Arvon for hosting Foyle Young Poets' residencies; Bloodaxe Books, Candlestick Press, Divine Chocolate, Forward Arts Foundation, Ignition Press, Nine Arches Press, Out-Spoken Press, and Poems on the Underground for providing winners' prizes.

Our thanks go to: judges Keith Jarrett and Maura Dooley for their dedication and their readiness to adapt to the circumstances of 2020; Matt Abbott and Theresa Lola, this year's award Patrons, for championing the competition; and the fantastic team of poets who helped the judging process – Jacqui Adeniji-Williams, Joshua Seigal, Phoebe Stuckes, Phoebe Thomson, Rachel Long, and Rachel Piercey.

We are grateful to Marcus Stanton Communications for raising awareness of the competition, and to our network of poets and educators across the UK for helping us to inspire so many young writers. Many thanks to artists James Brown for creating the anthology artwork, Imogen Foxell for her design bringing together the winning poems, and Chris Riddell for illustrating the top 15 poems.

Finally, we applaud the enthusiasm of the young people and teachers who make the Foyle Young Poets of the Year Award the success it is today.
foyleyoungpoets.org

Contents

Introduction

> *"If we had thought for a moment that this long year of Covid, of international unrest, of the tragedies that led renewed attention to Black Lives Matter might make humour impossible, or attention to very personal experience tricky, then how wrong we were. Poems came in from all over the world: poems of astonishing skill, poems of great tenderness, angry poems, poems that made me laugh and sometimes those were even all the same poem. What more could a reader ask?"*
>
> – Maura Dooley, Judge, Foyle Young Poets of the Year Award 2020

The Foyle Young Poets of the Year Award has been finding, celebrating and supporting the very best young poets from around the world since 1998. Founded and run by The Poetry Society, the award has been supported by the Foyle Foundation since 2001 and is firmly established as the key competition for young poets aged between 11 and 17 years.

This anthology features poems by the top 15 winners of the Foyle Young Poets of the Year Award 2020 and celebrates the names of the 85 commended poets. The winning poems were chosen by poets Maura Dooley and Keith Jarrett. In a competitive year for the award, judge Keith Jarrett commented: "It's been a privilege judging this year's prize. At a time when so many of us have been physically separated from friends and family, I've felt connected to thousands of young voices from around the world. The poems have been passionate, political, tender, troubling, humorous and, in many cases, brave."

All of the poems in this anthology were written by writers aged 11–17 at the time of writing. They demonstrate an extraordinary linguistic and emotional sophistication of which any established poet would be proud. Although rooted in the unsettling circumstances of 2020, this anthology has the capacity to transcend the year that birthed it: the collective wisdom offered here will stay with the reader long after they have put this volume down.

The events of 2020 play out across these pages: in her poem '*///Total///*', sixteen-year-old Anna Gilmore Heezen reflects defiantly on the anxiety of receiving exam results in an academic year disrupted by Covid-19; and the Black Lives Matter movement underpins 'the Race Card' by fourteen-year-old Lauren Lisk, and 'Found' by seventeen-year-old Zara Meadows. Questions of race and cultural heritage are also explored by seventeen-year-old Victoria Fletcher, who describes a treasure trove of "polski sklep" in 'A Little Bit of Poland in Sudbury Hill', and by sixteen-year-old Indigo Mudbhary, whose poem 'Brown Girl' examines what it means to have brown skin in America today. Sixteen-year-old Preesha Jain's poem, 'my grandmother', is a moving illustration of the sadness and indignity of cultural alienation within the poignantly quotidian environment of a supermarket.

In fact, supermarkets provide the setting for two other poems in this anthology: in 'Barcodes', thirteen-year-old Anna Winkelmann charts a touching conversation between two strangers, reminding us of the simple human desire for recognition; and seventeen-year-old Maia Siegel injects a touch of the surreal into 'The Kroger Car-Loading Service', in which an error at the checkout reveals the intersection between humour and desperation. If supermarkets seem to grace these pages with an unlikely frequency, we might recall that these poems were generated in a period when shops in many countries were forced to ration their supplies, key workers were applauded, and domesticity took on new dimensions.

From staying close to home to casting out into the wider world, fifteen-year-old Daniel Wale reflects evocatively on environmental change in 'Navajo Roads', while eleven-year-old Leandra Li's 'The Leshan Giant Buddha' boldly situates humanity within a larger existential context. Fifteen-year-old Imogen Beaumont revisits literary history in 'The Sound of Shakespeare's Women', a deft and canny poem that gives voice to the Bard's silenced heroines.

Elsewhere, seventeen-year-old Libby Russell also shines a light on the overlooked: 'Love Poem to Young Offenders Support Workers' is a subtle and succinct assertion of the power of community. Meanwhile, seventeen-year-old Brigitta McKeever strikes a darker tone in her poem 'Polaris', a rich exploration of truths exposed and things left unsaid.

Ultimately, the thread that binds all of these poems is the value they place on human connection. Nowhere is this more evident than in seventeen-year-old Linnet Drury's poem, 'Julia', in which familiarity and loss are evoked with heartbreaking accuracy. The solace of familiarity is similarly what characterises seventeen-year-old Em Power's 'CANBURY GARDENS AS A PROSE POEM DOMINATED BY THE WORD 'LIKE'', in which friendship takes centre-stage as the defining comfort of the age. As Em puts it, "what am I even meant to do – not love everyone? That's difficult, in times like these."

When we look back at 2020 in years to come, we may reflect on the political turbulence and epidemiological turmoil which cast a shadow over the year. This anthology brings together some of the most courageous young voices today. It is striking that the emerging generation never shies away from troubling times, but creates poems which offer space for reflection, humour, passion, solidarity, and hope.

Lauren Lisk
the Race Card

People always excuse racism with the phrase
"Stop using the race card" as if
The exploitation of blacks
The use of an infamous six letter word
Is all
A game
Like I could use my race card to
Make *happy families* of
All those who have lost
A brother
A sister
A parent
A child
Like I could use my race card to
Win this game of *top trumps*
And defeat what some may call kakistocracy
In one of the largest
Yet most broken countries in the world
Like I could use my race card
To stop this *game of life* where
People are seen as pawns
Through a lens of black and white
And protesting seems like a *trivial pursuit*
So how can I *articulate* to you
The fact that this is true?
If I did have a race card
I wouldn't roll the dice
Of wasting it on you.

Linnet Drury
Julia
(after Louisa Adjoa Parker)

Instead of you dying, why don't
you come round to ours. We'll tell
you we're ready by calling your
home and hanging up after three rings.
We'll hand you folded card takeaway menus,
pretend to look through them then reel out the
usual; garlic beansprouts with
mushroom curry, as if you had just
decided then and there, with
a sly chuckle. You'll pull three
movies, two cowboy one alien,
out of your worn black sack of
a handbag. You'll leave us late, for
we'll only start watching
the chosen film after a long discussion
about being a nun, your favourite
French abbeys. I'll pour you a drink
as you and my mother reminisce.
I'll watch you through the glass
of *something stronger*, crazy waves
of massive white hair. I'll be trying to
place the way you convey comfort, notice
how you always screw your
eyes in sympathy. Me and mum
will taxi you at 7am to
Easter service, the only people in
Oxford at dawn except the one

jogger. You always supply the change. You
won't have been the most sudden
death I heard of, via email. The
last time I see you won't be
leaving the cinema at 10pm, you so
excited Harrison Ford returned
for the final film, you telling us
I'm walking too slow, you
should run and catch up with the others
in your matter of fact way.
The last words we say to
you won't be *but this feels*
like the movies, where the old hand
tells the hero go on
without me, I'll only hold you
back and they are never seen
again? You won't say goodbye in your even more
matter of fact way and leave,
back into the ether, you'll
be sitting there at the Odeon
café next time, exactly fifteen minutes early
as usual.

Leandra Li
The Leshan Giant Buddha
(after Marilyn Chin)

step step step to the giant Buddha
made with the blood of three generations
and the eyes of the monk Hai Tong
made to calm the turbulent waters
so that the ships could sail smoothly
make your sacrifices to the Buddha
because nothing comes without a price
step step step to the giant Buddha

climb climb climb up the great stone steps
two hundred and seventy eight in number
more than just a mere tourist attraction
a symbolism of the long years passed
reminding us that the past will live on
battling weather wind, rain, hail, and sun
the statue still stands proud and tall
climb climb climb up the great stone steps

o holy Buddha answer me
will you still live on
when all of us are dead and gone?

Daniel Wale
Navajo Roads

A thick perfume of hot leather seats hangs
heavy in the air, which drags out
scraping melodies through an open window and
I – hand on the wheel – use up
a little more of man's hydrocarbon quota.
I sweat like a pig; the acrid fluid could fill
a lager can to its corroded brim. The chime of
falling coins has echoed long in these metallic walls.
Two hundred years ago, that Mercedes was my horse. Two hundred
years ago, its chassis of bone lay in the dust. Bleached legacies
leaked from a bullet hole as you dragged me deeper,
further through salted earth. Two thousand
nail-strikes ago, the tracks – your steel blankets,
hot and sick – left us choking in your wake.

Anna Winkelmann
Barcodes

Cars come and go in a swirling river
Of beeping horns and flashing lights

Marilyn pushes her trolley towards the window
Towards the checkout, ignoring offers of help from
Youths who think the whole world, and more, belongs to them

It's late, and the queue disappears soon enough under
The withering eyes of the evening

The checkout lady is no more than twenty-five,
Kids still in university, working part-time to cover all the bills.

She has a vague, nice smile fixed on her face, even
When Marilyn misplaces her broccoli for the second time

"My husband invented those,"
Marilyn says, and the checkout lady's eyes widen in surprise

"Oh. I didn't know that someone had invented them," "Well, surely someone must of. People don't talk about that kind of thing. Not anymore,"

George came up with the idea of a square. He perfected the idea: Credit? None

No one ever knew about the barcodes. It was me who told People that, yes my husband invented the barcode They would assume we were rich, assume that I was lying or just be kind of shocked,"

The checkout lady looks at Marilyn in a new kind of light The kind of light that comes from a scanner when it Recognises a barcode

"Well, I think they should."

Imogen Beaumont
The Sound of Shakespeare's Women

If Juliet was silenced
amongst a patriarchal nightmare and
Lavinia was two hands down
with no tongue to tell their tale and
Ophelia was driven to madness
with no sense left to speak and
Cordelia was shunned by her father,
her pointless words falling on deaf ears and
Desdemona's desperate truth
was shouted down by whispered lies,

Then Will's trying to tell us something.

Preesha Jain
my grandmother

my grandmother
wears silk sarees
woven with soft threads from India
stained with rich indigo dye;
tiny peacocks perch in the folds
and flecks of gold adorn them like jewels
sparkling with every movement.
a red bindi sits between her brows – she's a queen.
but in Tesco
she's an obscurity in the spice aisle.

my grandmother
has silver hair
plaited in intricate patterns
with garlands of yellow marigolds
tucked into the strands
accompanied with a sprinkling
of sweet-smelling jasmine flowers:
the marriage of the sun and moon –
but in Sainsbury's
she's an oddity amongst the frozen chapattis.

my grandmother
speaks in hindi
the language of saffron mangoes,
and fragrant blushing lotuses;
it flows like the ganga with
praises like honeyed rose petals

and even the stinging cusses like a biting karela
sound like a nightingale song.
but her broken English
in Morrisons
reduces her to suspicious looks
at the pickle shelf.

Victoria Fletcher
A Little Bit of Poland in Sudbury Hill

Dear Lord, I thank you for the polski skleps –
the strip-lights' thrum above the counters
thick with meat that prune-faced women slap
as they walk past; fondle the tomatoes
ripe, round, earth-dusty in their plastic crates;
eye up the bargains, the joyous promotions –
Promocja! Oferta! One-time special discount rates! –
and go through the housewife-gone-shopping motions:
the wheedle, the barter, demand and bark
for a pound off here, a bit more there
and survey the brands – Łaciate, Olewnik and Tymbark –
brands you'd be hard-pressed to find elsewhere,
slug-pickles swimming in emerald brine, treasures
each bringing joy beyond Englishmen's measure.

Anna Gilmore Heezen

///Total///

****

All the slow summer long £9.99
I have been living £6.90
in a glass jar of anxiety £16.90
and dreading £7.68
a day in August £6.57
when a devious envelope £12.90
with a barbed paper tongue £3.76
will slither through the door £2.46
to determine my fate £6.83
with only a few £5.80
letters: grades that might £5.45
be as sharp as blades £9.90
or as soft as rising dough. £5.67
At the end of the day, is this £3.54
all that I amount to? £12.80
Five letters on a flimsy £6.53
ghost of paper? £6.45
The narrowest indication £3.87

God, these £1.65
endless days of waiting . . . . :£8.76
and balancing on these tenterhook. £17.76
cobweb tightropes just won't do, ...£4.50
they just won't do. £14.90

****

I don't want to be calculated £8.76
counted £6.84
or summed up £7.36
in cold numbers and letters £3.56
that are typed by robotic fingers £4.90
that have no grace nor growth £23.90
because I am breathtakingly. £16.00
three dimensional, and £5.35
to total me £2.95
would be like £0.90
trying to add up the breeze . . . .£???.???

****

//Please retain receipt for your records//

Brigitta McKeever
Polaris

slit through the
belly and you will find
hot air, slippery fat, rabbit bones,
a beer belch swallowed.
ask him what he has done,
and he will say / nothing.

flush out the acid
and you will see what it has
ravaged. what remains of the forest
is its rot; of its birds, a feather.
ask him what can be done,
and he will say / nothing.

break open the chest
if you desire gold, oil, bleach.
let it smother you and see how
your skin blisters, your eyes turn
to dust, the rib cages nothing.
ask him what he has gained,
and he will say / everything.

(   )

burrow into his palm and
drain your milk; the North Star
thrashes in his paper folds.
let it blind you and you will see
the narrow skull of a boy, his

hollow cheeks ruddy, the bullet
between his eyes bleeding light.
ask him what he regrets,
and he will say /

Libby Russell
Love Poem to Young Offenders Support Workers

Here, where the streetlights have seen
more than any expert, there is a currency
in the green ghosts of cheap chains hidden under collars,
or in knowing somebody's brother from school,
or in the phone numbers of people who know
how to scoop up boys spilling out onto pavements,
their limbs limp as weeds, without calling for sirens
and warrants and lights; people who know
what to say to young men with grey faces
trembling blood onto paving stones,
and how to empty their hands without trouble. Here,
where there are no newspapers, talk is never cheap.
There is a currency in handlebar seats, and boys know
the value of dragging each other home.

Zara Meadows
Found

d'y'see your man there, in the –
in the grounds of the city hall,
d'y'hear he used to be a slaver?
kept slaves 'n that, sold thum
as well i think i read.
an'd'y'hear there's a bunch of themins
– themins at that owl protest the other
week – want 'im taken down?

          aye i did read that an all
          bit of a joke if you ask me
          not sayin' a agree wi slaves
          slavery, a mean a don't agree wi it
          but sure every man an his dog were
          at it in them days, sure what's the need
          goin tearin down our history, our culture
          sure it won't change the fact that it
          happened like – and do you know what else –
          it's themins, them same radicals
          want to collapse that wee man in the grounds
          of the city hall, that'd be sweet wi it bein'
          replaced wi a statue of
          Stalin, err some shite
          an sure didn' he own slaves an all?

Em Power
CANBURY GARDENS AS A PROSE POEM DOMINATED BY THE WORD 'LIKE'

I smirk at the middle-aged lady walking by, her eyes glinting like: *Yeah, gals, I'm with you.*
The sky is so blue my eyes hurt. There's a big sun, like: your feet are gonna burn inside your
shoes. I tell Ann and Sanjula that's what they get for wearing leather boots on a day like this.
Talia wades in the river, ankle deep, and I choose not to mention the needles. Like my mother
says: tetanus adds character. We all have to turn and shout: *You can't piss in that bush,
the fishermen will see you,* and Charlotte spends like, an entire hour finding a public toilet.
A homeless guy asks if we have any papers and Finn gives him like a whole pack of Rizla.
For a few minutes we're so convinced this white woman in sunglasses is going to call
the police on us, like being young and sitting is a crime. I tell Ceana: *Put your hands in my
hair. It's so soft. Feel it.* We mix our fruit boba with rosé like *isn't this the funniest shit ever!?*
Sanjula keeps eating rocks, like – no, yeah, literal rocks. Ann says it's like dealing with a toddler.
Talia and Elizabeth play a brutal game of footsie. The walk back to the bus station is long and hot.
I freeze and ask Charlotte to take photos of me with the bridge-side graffiti reading **BENNY.**
I know no one called Benny. Someone has a pink lighter covered in Sanrio stickers. Lars asks if it
still burns – my chest that is – not the sun. Now the sun is setting, and cool. When did it get that
way? Like, one minute it's day and then it's over. I have to lie face down in the grass 'cause
Elizabeth quotes that Ilya Kaminsky line like: *But with whom can you sit in water?* Or maybe I
lie face up, towards the sky. Ann tries to embarrass me the night after, says something like: *You
kept making us read your sappy fucking poems.* I cringe a suitable amount, but it's hard to care.
Like, what am I even meant to do – not love everyone? That's difficult, in times like these.

Maia Siegel
The Kroger Car-Loading Service

The grocery boy loaded her car
with twenty free-range chicken
breasts. She did not discover this
until she was back home, after
she had cloroxed every plastic Kroger
bag he could've held. She hadn't asked
for twenty, she'd asked for two and a pack
of paper towels. He hadn't given her
the paper towels and so, she thought, he gave
her eighteen extra breasts to make up for it. She
tried to sell the breasts on Facebook, ten bucks
apiece. She said she would accept Venmo
or Paypal, so no money would have to reach
across hands. No bidders. She looked up recipes
that used inane amounts of bird meat:
a pot pie, a noodle soup, a sandwich
with breasts as bread. She couldn't eat them
fast enough, so she started padding her bra
and briefs with the defrosting cutlets,
taking mirror shots where her ass looked
a couple inches thicker. She sent these pics
to every ex in her phone, even the ones who
had grown neckbeards. The house started to stink
from the chicken strip mobile she had put up
in the kitchen. It made no sound except that of meat
knocking into itself. She called the Kroger. She said
My grocery boy did a fabulous job. How can I tip
him? The woman on the phone gave her
the boy's address, said *We're not supposed to*

take tips but we've all almost cried and we got here
at four in the morning, so I think he'd accept.
She hung up, she breaded the final cutlets in
money, in sanitized bills. Cutlets in parchment
stamped with the heads of presidents. She gently
dropped them into an envelope, sent them
to the boy. She thought maybe
she was in love with him. She started
making plans to paper the inside of her trunk
with nude pictures of herself, or
the photos where the cutlets made her ass
look big. She shivered every time she imagined
him opening the trunk, all of her naked meat
staring back, him placing the defrosting
chicken meat over her like a dress,
like a negligee, like a shroud.

Indigo Mudbhary
Brown Girl
(inspired by Jamaica Kincaid's 'Girl')

"The mission of the United States is one of benevolent assimilation."
  – President William McKinley

practice your Nepali three times a day; don't ever forget your mother tongue; always speak English outside the house or people will think you're a terrorist; here's how to fold dough into a samosa; here's how to make mattar paneer; here's how to make the perfect momo; here's how to make the perfect momo sauce; here's how to make a peanut butter sandwich for school so the other kids don't make fun of you; here's how to wrap a sari; here's where to put your bindi; here's how to cry during a Bollywood movie; here's how to smile and nod when a white boy makes jokes about eating with your hands; here's how to get good grades; always tell your relatives you want to be a doctor even if you don't want to; never have sex or do drugs until you're at least thirty-five; here's how to fulfill your father's big American dream; don't worry about slurs because even though they say Paki here they don't do it too often; here's how to be an American; here's how to be Nepalese; always be more Nepalese than American but don't be too Nepalese or people will think you're a fucking curry muncher and we can't have that; here's how to say namaste to your auntie; here's how to say namaste to your uncle; here's how to say namaste to someone you want to be friends with; here's how to say namaste to someone you don't like at all; here's how to make thukpa; here's how to make a mandala; always buy sand for a mandala from Michael's because they have the best colored sand in America at least; here's how to not seem too American when you visit your relatives; here's how to not seem too Nepalese at school; always laugh politely when someone confuses Nepal with Naples even if it annoys you; here's how to point out Nepal on a map for white people; here's how to turn a prayer wheel; never give food to a monkey even if it's cute; this is where you put your statue of ganesha; this is where you put your statue of ganesha when friends come over; this is how you pray to a god; this is how you pray to multiple gods; this is how you ask a god for something; this is how you ask multiple gods for something; here's how to light a diya; here's how to be a good Auntie; here's how to be a good cousin; don't be mean to white people who say Nepal is basically India, they don't know any better; don't be mean to white people; don't be mean to white men; don't be mean to powerful white people; just don't be mean to white people; here's how to place an offering at a temple; here's how to receive tikka; don't wipe your tikka off your forehead even if it itches; stay calm during airport security screenings or else you're essentially a terrorist; here's how to explain the difference between hinduism and hindi to a white person but it's better if you don't at all; don't dye your hair it never looks good on brown people; here's how to whiten your skin just a little bit; here's how to approach an elephant; here's how to approach an elephant in the room; here's how to make the perfect dal; here's how to make the perfect dal bhat; always finish your food; here's how to be a brown person in America but really you should just try to be more white because we don't want anyone thinking that you're some fucking terrorist.

Foyle Young Poets of the Year 2020

The top 15 winners: Anna Gilmore Heezen • Anna Winkelmann • Brigitta McKeever • Daniel Wale • Em Power • Imogen Beaumont • Indigo Mudbhary • Lauren Lisk • Leandra Li • Libby Russell • Linnet Drury • Maia Siegel • Preesha Jain • Victoria Fletcher • Zara Meadows

The commended poets: Aashka Vardhman • Ahana Banerji • Ailsa Morgan • Alyssa Theofanidis • Amala Sangha • Amélie Nixon • Anisha Jaya Minocha • Anne Kwok • April Egan • Arabella Green • Artemis Fernihough • Ayra Ahmad • Blessing Verrall • Celeste Herriotts • Celia Mostachfi • Charlotte Hughes • chenrui • Claudia Quin • Connie Alvarez • Divyasri Krishnan • Elise Withey • Eliza Sinclair Kidd • Elsie Hayward • Elyse Thomas • Emily Man • Emily Ng • Erin Hateley • Eshan Fadi • Euan Sinclair • Eve Calvey • Eve Wright • Evie Collins • Florence Bullion • Francesca Morgan • Freya Leech • Georgina Cary • Grace Phillips • Hannah Eve Kilgore • Helen Roth • Hope Vaughan • Iona Mandal • Jaewon Chang • Jamie See • Janiru Liyanage • Jeanne Everett Meraioth • Jennah Agha • Jonathan Truong • Kate O'Brien • Kerensa Pickering • Kitty Joyce • Kitty Robinson • Lilly Jane Nolan • Lily Celeste Ashby • Liv Goldreich • Lucy Stone • Lucy Waters • Maddie Harris • Madison Averill • Martha Iris Blue • Martha Routledge • Martine Maugüé • Maureen Onwunali • Merrie LeMaître Nugent • Olajuwon-Alhaytham Abdullah Adedokun • Oreva Esalomi • Patricia Ssonko Nalule • Phaedra Wright • Phoebe Z. Barowitz • Priya Abularach • Priya Shrivastva • Ran Zhao • Remi Seamon • Sabrina Guo • Saima Begum • Samiya Saif Ullah • Sarah Fathima Mohammed • Serrina Zou • Sinead Bruce • Sinéad O'Reilly • Sung Cho • Theodora Shillito • Tom Griffin • Vidula Selvan • Zayaan Jamil • Zoe Dorothy Leary

Read the winning and commended poems online

The online anthologies of winning and commended Foyle Young Poets of the Year 2020 are available at **bit.ly/foyleyoungpoets**

About us

The Poetry Society

The Poetry Society is the leading poetry organisation in the UK. For over 100 years we've been a lively and passionate source of energy and ideas, opening up and promoting poetry to an ever-growing community of people. We run acclaimed international poetry competitions for adults and young people and publish *The Poetry Review*, one of the most influential poetry magazines in the English-speaking world. With innovative education and commissioning programmes, and a packed calendar of performances and readings, The Poetry Society champions poetry for all ages. **poetrysociety.org.uk**

The Foyle Foundation

The Foyle Foundation is an independent grant-making trust supporting UK charities which, since its formation in 2001, has become a major funder of the Arts and Learning. The Foyle Foundation has invested in the Foyle Young Poets of the Year Award since 2001, one of its longest partnerships. During this time it has trebled its support and enabled the competition to develop and grow to become one of the premier literary awards in the country. **foylefoundation.org.uk**

Help young writers thrive

The Poetry Society's work with young people and schools across the UK changes the lives of readers, writers and performers of poetry, developing confidence and literacy skills, encouraging self-expression and opening up new life opportunities. Support us by donating at **poetrysociety.org.uk/donate**

About the Foyle Young Poets of the Year Award

The Foyle Young Poets of the Year Award is at the core of The Poetry Society's extensive education programme. In 2020, the competition received almost 16,000 poems from over 6,000 young poets from 118 territories. From these poems, this year's judges, Maura Dooley and Keith Jarrett, selected 100 winners: 15 top poets and 85 commended poets. The competition's scale and global reach shows what a huge achievement it is to be selected as one of our winners.

All 100 winners of the Foyle Young Poets of the Year Award receive a range of brilliant prizes, including a year's youth membership of The Poetry Society and a goody bag stuffed full of books donated by our generous supporters. The Poetry Society continues to nurture winners throughout their careers, providing publication, performance and development opportunities, and access to a paid internship programme. The top 15 poets also receive further sustained mentoring.

Alongside the annual competition, the award programme includes a number of initiatives to encourage and enable young writers. We distribute free teaching resources to every secondary school in the UK, share tips from talented teachers and arrange poet-led workshops in areas of low engagement. The winners' anthology, together with an online anthology of the 85 commended poems, is distributed free to schools, libraries, reading groups, and poetry lovers across the UK and the world.

It's not only young people who are celebrated as part of the award: their teachers also receive special recognition for inspiring the next generation of poets. Each year The Poetry Society identifies a new cohort of 'Teacher Trailblazers' through the award, for individuals showing outstanding commitment to poetry in the classroom. Young people play a vital role, nominating their most inspiring teachers when they enter the competition. In 2020–21, we are delighted to collaborate with Gareth Ellis from Whitley Bay High School, North Tyneside, and Stephanie Nobes from Hounsdown School, Hampshire, to share their enthusiasm for poetry with the wider teaching community.

The Foyle Young Poets of the Year Award plays an influential role in shaping contemporary British poetry. Former winners regularly go on to publish full poetry collections and are often recognised in significant national competitions for adults. In 2020, for instance, Caroline Bird won the Forward Prize for Best Collection and was shortlisted for the Costa Poetry Award with *The Air Year* (Carcanet), and Martha Sprackland was shortlisted for the Forward Prize for Best First Collection and the Costa Poetry Award with *Citadel* (Pavilion Poetry). Theophilus Kwek's new collection *Moving House* was published by Carcanet. Bloodaxe published Phoebe Stuckes's first full collection, *Platinum Blonde*; Phoebe also won The Poetry Society's Geoffrey Dearmer Prize. One of the winning poems from the Foyle Award, 'Peckham Rye Lane' by Amy Blakemore (2007), is now a set text in the updated Edexcel GCSE poetry anthology ('Collection D: Belonging'). Poet and critic Jade Cuttle was a judge for the Costa Book Awards, and launched her debut album of poetic-folk, *Algal Bloom*. Sarah Fathima Mohammed won first prize and Ife Olatona was commended in the Ledbury Poetry Festival Poetry Competition 2020.

We are confident that the most recent winners of the competition will go on to reach similarly dizzying heights, and we look forward to discovering yet more fantastic young poets in years to come. If you're a young writer reading this anthology, enter the Foyle Young Poets of the Year Award 2021 and you could follow in the footsteps of some of the most successful poets writing today.

Further opportunities for young people

As well as the Foyle Young Poets of the Year Award, The Poetry Society offers lots of ways for young people to engage with writing for the page or exploring spoken word.

If you're a young person who really enjoys creative writing, check out **Young Poets Network**, The Poetry Society's free online platform for poets worldwide up to the age of 25. It's for everyone interested in poets and poetry – whether you've just started out, or you're a seasoned reader and writer. You'll find features, challenges and competitions to inspire your own writing, as well as new writing from young poets, and advice and guidance from the rising and established stars of the poetry scene. Young Poets Network also offers a list of competitions, magazines and writing groups that particularly welcome young writers. For updates about poets, poetry, competitions, events and more, like us on Facebook and follow us on Twitter @youngpoetsnet and Instagram @thepoetrysociety **youngpoetsnetwork.org.uk**

Aspiring writers and poetry enthusiasts aged 11–18 can also buy **Poetry Society Youth Membership**. Members receive poetry goodies, discounts towards opportunities for feedback, The Poetry Society's newspaper *Poetry News*, and other benefits.
poetrysociety.org.uk/membership

Do you have an inspiring teacher? Tell us about them

We want to connect with brilliant teachers who care as much about poetry as we do, so we can continue to reach young poets like you. If your teacher inspired you to write or read poetry, and you think we should know about them, email **fyp@poetrysociety.org.uk**

Please tell us your teacher's name and the name of your school, and include a sentence or two about how your teacher has inspired you.

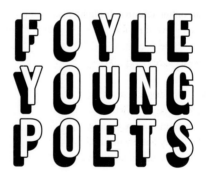

Schools and The Poetry Society

Foyle Award teaching resources, including lesson plans and online versions of the winning and commended Foyle Young Poets anthologies, are available on our website at **poetrysociety.org.uk/fypresources**

Poetryclass lesson plans and activities, covering all Key Stages and exploring many themes and forms of poetry, are easy to search and free to download. Each resource has been created by our team of poet-educators and teachers, with hands-on experience of developing an enthusiasm for poetry in the classroom. Find Poetryclass on our dedicated site: **resources.poetrysociety.org.uk**

Page Fright is an online resource, bringing historical poetry to life with contemporary spoken word performances. Page Fright poets such as Benjamin Zephaniah perform their own work, and explore historical poems afresh. **poetrysociety.org.uk/pagefright**

Poets in Schools help develop an understanding of and enthusiasm for poetry across all Key Stages. Whether you are looking for a one-off workshop or a long-term residency, an INSET session for staff or a poet-led assembly, The Poetry Society will find the right poet for you. Online and in-person options available. **poetrysociety.org.uk/education**

School Membership connects your school with all that poetry has to offer. School members receive books, resources, posters, *Poetry News* and *The Poetry Review* (secondary only), as well as free access to our Poets in Schools service. **poetrysociety.org.uk/membership**

Follow us on Twitter @PoetryEducation or sign up to our schools e-bulletin by emailing educationadmin@poetrysociety.org.uk

Enter the Foyle Young Poets of the Year Award 2021
Judges: Clare Pollard and Yomi Ṣode

Enter your poems – change your life! The Foyle Young Poets of the Year Award 2021 is open to any writer aged 11 to 17 (inclusive) until the closing date of 31 July 2021. The competition is completely free to enter and poems can be on any theme or subject.

Prizes include poetry goodies, mentoring, places on a week-long Arvon writing course, publication in a prestigious anthology, and much more. Winners also benefit from ongoing support and encouragement from The Poetry Society via publication, performance and internship opportunities.

How to enter: please read the updated competition rules, published in full at foyleyoungpoets.org. You can send us your poems online through our website, or by post. If you are aged 11–12 you will need permission from a parent or guardian to enter. You can enter more than one poem, but please concentrate on drafting and redrafting your poems – quality is more important than quantity. Entries cannot be returned under any circumstances so please keep copies. For more information, visit the rules section at **foyleyoungpoets.org**

School entries: teachers can enter sets of poems by post or online using our simple submission form. Every school that enters 25 students or more will receive a £50 discount on our Poets in Schools service.

Want a **FREE set of anthologies, resources and posters** for your class? Email your name, address and request to **fyp@poetrysociety.org.uk**

For full rules and instructions, visit foyleyoungpoets.org